Read•A•Picture
COLORS &
NUMBERS

By Burton Marks
Illustrated by Paul Harvey

JOSHUA MORRIS PUBLISHING

COUNTING COLOURS

1 red ,

2 purple ,

3 yellow wearing new coats.

4 blue swimming in the sea,

5 brown swinging in a .

6 orange  ,

7 black ,

8 pink

learning to dance.

9 green

riding on a train,

10 white

walking in the rain.

WHAT THINGS ARE RED?

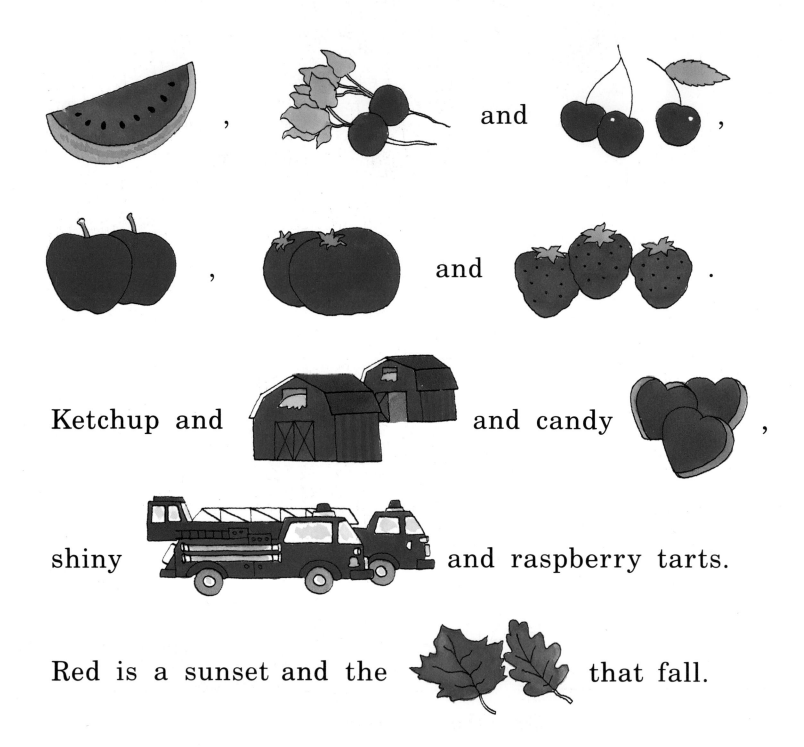

Ketchup and ⬛ and candy ❤,

shiny 🚒 and raspberry tarts.

Red is a sunset and the 🍁 that fall.

Perhaps red is the prettiest colour of all.

FIND-A-PICTURE

Somewhere in this picture are:

1 **2** **3** **4** and **5** . Can you find them?

WHAT THINGS ARE YELLOW?

Canaries and [pears] and vanilla custard,

and [cheese] and hot dog mustard!

and [chicks] and baby chicks,

and [corn] and lemon sticks.

Yellow is candlelight, and yellow is the

that shines when I go outside to have fun.

SUE'S SHOES

One day a  whose name was Sue

exclaimed, "I think I've lost a  ."

She cried out loud:

Boo hoo, boo hoo!
What will I do
with just one  ?

Just then a  called out, "Yoo-hoo,"

and straight into the room he flew—

Oh, lucky you—
I found your  .

But my shoe is red.
This 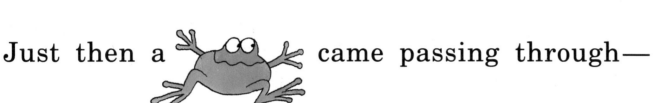 is blue.
It positively
will not do.

That's true, that's true,
but let's review.
Instead of **1**
you now have **2**!

Just then a 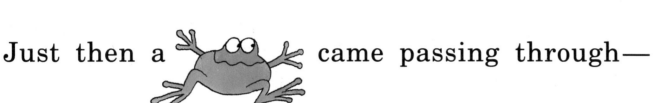 came passing through—

My dear friend Sue
I brought for you
a purple
now toodle-oo.

Oh dear me!
How can this be?
Instead of **2**
I now have **3**.

And then a  came through the .

I have just what you're looking for—
a yellow almost brand-new.

No more, no more
I do implore!
Instead of **3**
I now have **4**.

But then a  arrived…

Oh dear, I fear
here's number **5**.

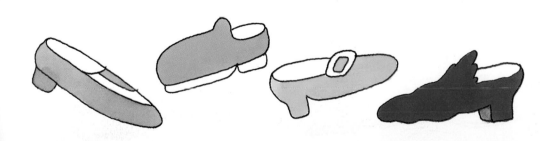

I just heard about your missing  so I brought a new green one for you.

Now Sue was not ungrateful,
and she really was amused
at being the new owner
of so many pretty

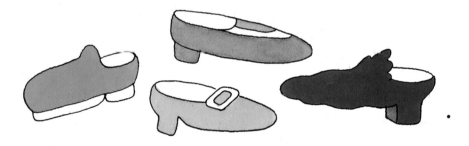

Which prompted her to say:

Now I can wear
a different pair
every single day!

WHAT THINGS ARE BLUE?

Blue jeans, 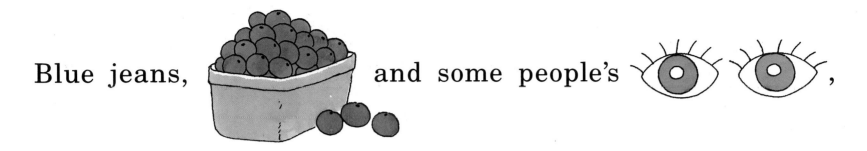 and some people's ,

blue 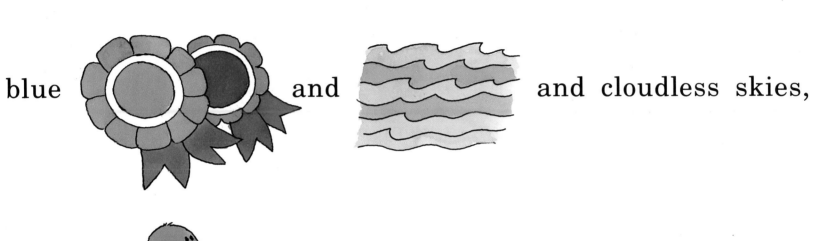 and and cloudless skies,

blue 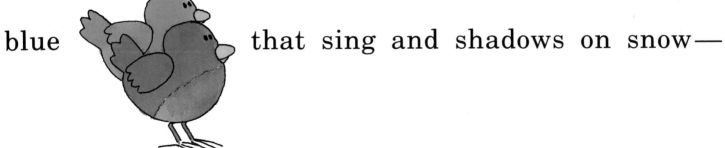 that sing and shadows on snow—

now how many more blue things do you know?

OWL'S COUNTING GAME

Here's a counting game that's fun. Let's see if you can count to one.

That's easy! I just say **1** shining  and then I'm done.

Now tell me who can count to two.

1 spool of

2 loaves of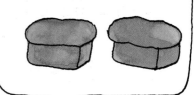

There's just one more thing
I need to know.
Can you count to five?
Ready? Let's go!

1 red

2 cuckoo

3 pairs of and matching

4 croaking

wearing top

5 barking

chasing **5**

THE RAINY DAY SURPRISE

Sometimes, on rainy days, Mother gave Tommy

a little surprise. "Will I get a surprise today?" asked

 as the 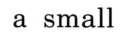 streamed down his bedroom  .

"I have a colourful surprise for you," said  .

She handed 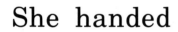 a small  . It was a

bright new box of 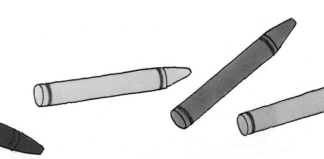 . "Let's see if you can draw

things that are the same colour as each 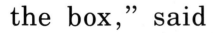 in

the box," said .

"I'll try," said  . "That sounds like fun."

First Tommy chose a  and drew the  .

Then he took a  and drew a  . Next

he used a to draw a and a

to draw  . He used the to draw a

Finally he used the to draw some  .

"Now can you draw a picture using every colour

in the box?" asked . thought for a

moment, then he started to draw.

Can you guess what Tommy drew?
Turn the page to find the answer.

"That's a perfect picture to draw for a rainy day," said .

WHAT THINGS ARE GREEN?

 and celery and pickles and 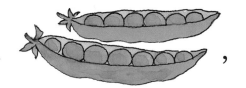 ,

 and  and big leafy  ,

 , olives, cabbage and 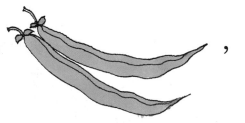 ,

grasshoppers, 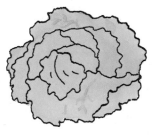 and evergreens.

Green is everywhere, or so it would seem;

how many things can *you* name that are green?

From 1 to 10, from  to ,

we p this

has been fun for U !